YOU
CAN BE
WHATEVER
YOU WANT,
GIRL!

A GIRL-POWER GUIDE AND
WORKBOOK TO HELP YOU
BOOST YOUR SELF-CONFIDENCE
AND ACHIEVE YOUR DREAMS—
WITH PRACTICAL EXERCISES,
TIPS, AND ADVICE

FlyingKids® Presents

YOU CAN BE WHATEVER YOU WANT, GIRL!

A girl-power guide and workbook to help you boost your self-confidence and achieve your dreams—with practical exercises, tips, and advice

Author: **Shira Halperin**
Editor: **Carma Graber**
Designer: **Nebojsa Dolovacki**
Writing assistance: **Jackie Hostetler**
Illustrations: **Oksana Melnychuk, Aaron Benjamin De Castro**

Published by FlyingKids® Limited, 2021

Visit us: www·theflyingkids·com
Contact us: leonardo@theflyingkids·com
ISBN: 978-1-910994-45-0
Copyright © 2021 Shira Halperin and FlyingKids® Limited

Acknowledgments: Page 28 – Greta Thunberg photo: European Parliament, CC BY 2.0, via Wikimedia Commons; Simone Biles photo: Agência Brasil Fotografias, CC BY 2.0, via Wikimedia Commons; Kamala Harris photo: Lawrence Jackson, public domain, via Wikimedia Commons.

TABLE OF CONTENTS

INTRODUCTION

> A girl should be two things: who and what she wants.
>
> — **Coco Chanel**

LIRI HERE!

I can't wait to get to know you!

Hey, Girl! My name is Liri! I have lots of big ideas and lots of big dreams! I bet you have some too. I'm excited to hear all about it and share some of my experiences along the way!

I used to be **the shy girl**. I used to think that everyone around me was smarter than me. I used to think it was harder for me to succeed than for all the other kids. It seemed like **I was always doubting myself**. I didn't have much confidence to try new things, whether that was new experiences or meeting new people.

Do you ever feel that way?

I knew I had some **talents** and **abilities**, but I wasn't exactly sure what they were or how to use them. I saw other kids around me succeeding at all the things I wished I had the courage to do. Sometimes I tried and gave up. Sometimes I didn't even try. I just felt like it was useless. It was all pretty frustrating.

I had dreams. I WANTED TO DO THINGS, but I wasn't sure I could—or even how to start.

BUT I DECIDED TO CHANGE!

Then slowly, step-by-step, I learned to change the things that had bothered me for as long as I could remember. After a while, some of the things that had seemed so scary didn't seem that scary anymore. I made new friends and **tried new things**. I learned how to **feel good about the things that used to bother me**.

And to feel good about me!

You're probably asking yourself—HOW? How did I make this change?

I did it by learning about myself. And I'm still learning! I love to LEARN and I love to keep changing for the better.

There are so many **tools** and **practices** that have helped me achieve the things I've always wanted to achieve.

I've been able to build new SKILLS that help me to **grow** and **keep learning**. I'm still developing and growing every day.

It feels awesome to be able to do the things I couldn't do before. Now I have the **courage** to try stuff I used to think I would never be able to do!

I believe I CAN DO IT! I believe in myself.

I've had such an incredible journey, filled with guidance and support from the people around me. Now it's my turn to pay it forward and **help guide you**! I want to help YOU to believe in YOU! If I learned how to do it, YOU CAN TOO! I'm inviting you to try.

All you have to do is trust your **heart**, open your **mind**, grab a **pen**, and keep **reading**!

This book is an INVITATION for a journey—and a tool to journal about your experiences.

I invite you, my dear friend.

It will be a JOURNEY we can travel together—and you can invite anyone else to join us at any time. This will be an adventure in **feeling good about yourself** and making yourself into an even MORE AMAZING YOUNG WOMAN!

It will be a JOURNAL to help you achieve all your goals!

This **journey** and this **journal** are dedicated to YOU, Girl! There is so much to learn, and there are so many tools that can help. In this book, I've tried to share with you everything I believe you'll need for your journey:

Inspiring THOUGHTS   Helpful TIPS   Practical TOOLS

I truly believe this book can help ANYONE, especially GIRLS filled with hopes and dreams!

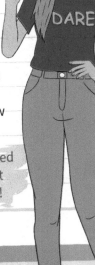

I have **tons of tools** to help you believe in yourself and achieve success—things that will be invaluable as you work toward achieving your dreams! I can't wait to show you how these tools will **help you set your goals**, **make them happen**, and never give up. When you have the right tools, learning and growing becomes so much easier!

Remember, it's a journey. Sometimes you'll see **quick progress** that is fun and easy to achieve. Sometimes **it takes time**. But never forget, I BELIEVE IN YOU. **You can do it!** Even if you're not completely sure about yourself right now, I know that you're SO SPECIAL.

I know you have some pretty **incredible qualities!** You just need to figure out **what they are** and then **develop them** in a smart way—a way that will lead you to success. YOU CAN DO IT, GIRL!

Now that you know all about me. Let's find out a little more about you.

What's your name?

How old are you?

Have you ever kept a journal before? If so, what did you use it for?

What are some things you do for fun?

How do you like to express yourself? Music? Drawing? Writing? More?

What's your all-time favorite movie, TV show, or series and why?

Who is your personal hero and why?

What are you hoping to achieve by completing this journey and journal?

Are you ready to take this journey with me?

Great! Let's get started!

PART 1

ALL ABOUT YOU!

> Knowing yourself is the beginning of all wisdom.
>
> — *Aristotle, Greek philosopher*

I'm going to start by telling you something magical. Maybe it's something you already know, or maybe not. Maybe you won't believe me. You might think I'm just telling you this because I don't really know you. But here's the thing … I know I'm right! Listen up! **YOU ARE AMAZING!** And **you can be whatever you want, Girl!**

 There is no one in this world quite like you.

You have tons of **GIFTS** and **ABILITIES** that are **unique to just you**.

These special qualities are the things that **make you simply AMAZING**.

And it's time to find out more about **YOUR QUALITIES**.

Sometimes you just need to **get to know yourself** a little bit better to see all the wonderful things **everyone else sees in you**.

And sometimes you need to **let others** see the things that you don't always share with the world. We can all be a little shy about sharing this stuff sometimes.

Even me!

> I want you, and the whole world, to understand just **how incredible you really are.**

Let's do a little exercise together.

YOUR SPECIAL QUALITIES

Think about *your* **special qualities**—your natural talents, your knowledge, your unique behaviors. What sets you apart from the crowd?

For some girls, these qualities may be super-easy to list. Others might not be sure exactly what to write. Either way, **it's okay**. Just take a few minutes and write what is **in your heart**. You can share your list with friends, family, or anyone else who can help you become the best you that you can be!

Paste a photo of yourself here

Now that you're starting to find your special qualities, let's chat about how you can take those qualities to the next level!

I know you're amazing. But guess what? You can be even **more amazing!** One of the most special things about you is the fact that you are **always learning** and **always growing**. If you want to be the best you can be, it's important that you learn a little (or a lot) about yourself. The best way to do this is to **SELF-REFLECT** on what you've discovered.

 SELF-REFLECTION, or as I like to call it, **SelfRe,** is one of the most important tools you can use in your everyday life.

WHAT DOES IT MEAN TO SELF-REFLECT OR SELFRE?

It just means that you pay attention to your **thoughts** and **emotions**. You can also SelfRe on the **decisions** you are making and the way you respond to different situations. You can SelfRe on how your **day went**—or maybe how you want your **day to go** tomorrow. There are lots and lots of times you can use SelfRe to help you out. Right now, you are going to use SelfRe to find out a little bit about yourself. So grab a pen and start the SelfRe!

You might think you can't SelfRe. Maybe you think it will be too hard. Well, guess what? If you filled out the bubbles around your photo on the last page, you are actually ALREADY using SelfRe! Listing your special qualities is a way of looking inside yourself and paying attention to exactly what is special about you. **Congrats, you've just SelfRe-ed!**

> ## "WHO IN THE WORLD AM I? AH, THAT'S THE GREAT PUZZLE."
>
> — *Lewis Carroll, British author of* Alice in Wonderland

11

Getting to Know Me questionnaire

Now let's get to know you even more. Take time to thoughtfully answer the questions below. Once you are done with the questionnaire, use the scoring key to figure out which category you match most closely.

1. When I have free time, I would rather ...
A. Catch up with friends at the local pizza place.
B. Curl up in my bed with a good book.
C. Engage in routines and traditions with family.
D. Listen to music online while I scroll through all the fun stuff on my phone.

2. When I feel stressed or overwhelmed, I like to ...
A. Talk with my parents or siblings about what may be bothering me.
B. Log on and express myself through blogs, vlogs, or other types of social media.
C. Unwind with a few close friends.
D. Find a quiet place to be alone with my thoughts.

3. My favorite way of expressing myself is by ...
A. Journaling, painting, writing music, or other solo crafts.
B. Planning celebrations or get-togethers.
C. Playing or creating computer games and applications.
D. Creating a cozy and pleasant environment around me.

4. On a typical day I usually wear ...
A. Jeans and a graphic T-shirt— casual works for me.
B. Joggers and a sweatshirt— being comfortable is key.
C. Latest fashions—keeping up with trends is important to me.
D. My own unique style—I love to mix and match and wear what feels good to me.

5. My idea of the perfect meal is ...
A. Home cooking shared around the table with my family.
B. Eating at a quiet place with one very close friend.
C. Being at a bustling restaurant with tons of friends and lots of great food.
D. Grabbing a burger and fries to munch on while I watch YouTube.

6. I would hate to miss ...
A. My grandparents' wedding anniversary.
B. My best friend's birthday party.
C. My favorite series dropping on a streaming platform.
D. The release date for the upgrade of my favorite video game.

7. When I grow up, I would love to be ...
A. A video game developer, animator, or computer programmer.
B. Anything that allows me to work from home, like being an author or a maker.
C. Owner of my own business so I can be my own boss.
D. A teacher, doctor, or other professional who helps and interacts with others.

8. My favorite person or people to be around are ...
A. Me, myself, and I.
B. My friends.
C. My online community.
D. My family.

Scoring Key:

To get your test results, look at the chart below and find the number of points that matches your answer to each question. For example, if you chose "A" for question 1, give yourself one point. If you chose "D" for question 2, add three more points, and so on. Continue to add your points for each question to get your final score (the total number of points you got for all the questions).

Question No.	1	2	3	4	5	6	7	8
No. of Points	A=1	A=4	A=3	A=2	A=4	A=4	A=2	A=3
	B=3	B=2	B=1	B=4	B=3	B=1	B=4	B=1
	C=4	C=1	C=2	C=1	C=1	C=3	C=3	C=2
	D=2	D=3	D=4	D=3	D=2	D=2	D=1	D=4

MY TOTAL POINTS:

What your score tells you about yourself:

8–13 points – You are a Social Butterfly:

Friends and social experiences are a big source of support for you. You like to share your achievements with your friends and have their support when you face challenges. You feel most comfortable having a wide social circle with many different types of people and experiences.

14–20 points – You are a Tech Girl with a Logical Side.

You are motivated by logic. You are fascinated with technology and its ability to help you connect and learn. You understand that science and technology can make life better and allow you to experience the world in a whole new way.

21–26 points – You are Independent and Loving It.

You feel that the best way to accomplish tasks and goals is by yourself. You pride yourself on your independence. Sometimes social situations can be a bit too much for you. You feel most comfortable recharging your batteries with a little "me time."

27–32 points – You are a Family-First Girl.

Family and home life are at the top of your list of priorities. When you need advice or support, the first person you turn to is a trusted family member. You are never quite so comfortable as when you cozy up at home with the people and things you love the most.

So? Any surprises? Did your answers usually fall under just one category, or were you all over the board? **One girl can definitely fall into lots of different categories!** You might find that you like to celebrate with friends but unwind by yourself. You can be a social butterfly and independent at the same time. Take a minute to SelfRe on all your special characteristics and the different categories they fall under. **Can you think of a specific example from your life in which you fall into two different categories?**

Part 2

BELIEVE IN YOURSELF

> To tell me what I can't do is to tell me what I will do.
>
> — *Anonymous*

 A huge key to success is BELIEVING IN YOURSELF. Huge! Believe that you can be whatever you want, Girl!

Before you start to learn and grow, you need to believe that YOU CAN DO IT—you can **believe in yourself.** Sometimes this can be more difficult than any other kind of learning, and it might even feel a little uncomfortable or scary. It's different than learning to play an instrument or learning a new subject at school. You are actually changing the way you think about yourself. And I know from experience, it's going to take some time!

> The more you're able to take small steps toward success, the more your confidence will grow, and the more you'll believe in yourself. This is a process. **Take your time, Girl. You can do it!** I should know—I've been there.

I like to think that I'm pretty confident now, but I wasn't always like this. In fact, when I was younger, there were lots of things I was afraid to do. I'll always regret not auditioning for my middle-school choir. I knew I was a good singer, but I was just so scared the choir teacher would reject me. I didn't have much confidence, and I couldn't stand the thought of failing, so **I didn't even try**.

The funny thing is, I probably would have made it. I guess I'll never know. But I will tell you this, I'd never let something like that stop me now. It took some time, but I've learned that trying, and sometimes failing, is just a part of life. You'll find that out too.

And if **YOU** believe in yourself, **OTHERS** will believe in you—which is awesome! But if you don't believe in yourself, it could be harder for the people around you to believe in you. And that could be a pretty big bummer.

The perfect combination for success is to believe in yourself and trust that others have confidence in you too! Now that's what I call a "win-win"! You'll get there! Believe me!

Your confidence areas

Now it's time to rate your self-confidence.

Every girl has certain areas in her life where she has **more** confidence, and other areas where she has **less** confidence.

Let's look at the areas where you have more self-confidence versus the areas where you're less confident.

If you feel you have a lot of self-confidence in an area, mark yourself high—like a 5. If you feel you have less self-confidence in an area, mark yourself low. There may be some areas where you feel your self-confidence is in the middle range—mark 2, 3, or 4.

MY SELF-CONFIDENCE AT SCHOOL: learning new subjects, interacting with teachers, maintaining organization, completing assignments

1	2	3	4	5

MY SELF-CONFIDENCE AT HOME: completing chores, waking up and going to bed on time

1	2	3	4	5

MY SELF-CONFIDENCE WITH FAMILY MEMBERS: spending time together, sharing about my day

1	2	3	4	5

MY SELF-CONFIDENCE AT AFTER-SCHOOL ACTIVITIES: attending practices, cooperating with others, my skill level

1	2	3	4	5

MY SELF-CONFIDENCE WITH MY FRIENDS: feeling accepted, accepting others, working to strengthen our relationships

1	2	3	4	5

Are there any other areas or specific situations you are more confident about?

Are there any other areas or specific situations you are less confident about?

It can be tough to be **honest** with yourself about this kind of thing. **I'm proud of you!** If you want to raise your confidence level in the areas where you marked yourself lower, you can actively work on that. You can keep those situations in mind as we talk later about setting and achieving goals.

What about people around you? Can you think of a time or situation when someone had confidence in you (Yippee!)?

Can you think of a time or situation when someone may have doubted your abilities or discouraged you from trying something new (Yuck!)?

I'm going to tell you a little secret. Sometimes the people around you may try to **protect you** because **they care about you.** Unfortunately, sometimes without even knowing it, they may make you feel like you can't do a certain thing, or that it's better not to even try. They may be **trying to prevent you from failing** and being hurt, and they may feel trying is too risky.

I'm going to tell you another little secret! Just because you don't feel completely confident at first, or someone else thinks you can't do something, **it doesn't mean you can't. GIVE IT A SHOT!**

Yes, it might be difficult.

Yes, you might fail.

But always remember—you can, and you should, try again.

Try until you succeed.

YOU CAN DO IT!

Do you remember a time when either you or someone else thought you couldn't do something, and you found you were actually able to succeed? Go, Girl! **How did you feel when you were finally successful?**

> It is confidence in our bodies, minds, and spirits that allows us to keep looking for new adventures.
>
> — *Oprah Winfrey, American media personality and entrepreneur*

As my grandma used to say: "You live in an **amazing world** during **an amazing time!** Lucky you, Girl! "

And she's right! There are more opportunities for girls and women than ever before. Women do **big things**, **important things**. It wasn't always like that in the past. But you can do anything you want to do—and you can be whatever you want, Girl! **ANYTHING**—I promise!

It's your turn, Girl!
Start thinking about what exactly it is that you want to do.

What do you dream of being someday? News flash! You don't have to wait until you're all grown up. There are lots of things you can do **NOW** to get started on your big dreams!

You can start small. **Do one thing to move forward** on your path to success. Like, maybe your big dream is to dance in a national ballet. Start small by attending one dance class.

Don't worry if this kind of planning seems a bit unfamiliar. We'll break this down together a little later. Always remember, even if you start small— DREAM BIG!

You will do incredible things!

It's time to explore those dreams through another SelfRe exercise. You're going to need a big mirror for this one. Keep this journal and something to write with handy too!

The Girl in the Mirror

Stand in front of a big mirror. What are five words that describe the girl you see in front of you?

1.
2.
3.
4.
5.

What are three things the girl in the mirror has done in the past that make her feel proud?

1.

2.

3.

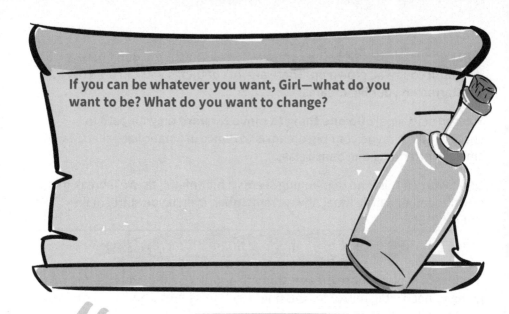

If you can be whatever you want, Girl—what do you want to be? What do you want to change?

> # DO THE THINGS YOU CANNOT DO.
>
> — *Eleanor Roosevelt, American political figure and former First Lady*

Do you remember that game we all used to play when we were younger called "**I dare you**"? The object of the game was usually for a friend to "dare" you to try something that may have been a little uncomfortable or unique, or may have even taken a bit of courage.

I dare you to run down the block while singing your favorite song as loud as you can.

I dare you to stand on your head for 30 seconds.

I dare you to jump off the high diving board at the swimming pool.

Sound familiar?

Remember how you felt after you completed the dare?

Excited. Proud. Brave.

Guess what? Dares aren't only for childhood games. You can still do things that are a little **uncomfortable**, a little **unique**, or that take a little bit of **courage**.

But now, you DARE YOURSELF!

Dare yourself to make a new friend at school. Feel excited!

Dare yourself to express your style and your vibe in a way that is comfortable and satisfying to you. Feel proud!

Dare yourself to try out for the track team, or the school play, or whatever it is that you've always wanted to do. Feel brave!

Dare yourself to be great! IT FEELS AMAZING!

Think about a few things YOU might dare yourself to do.

You might dare yourself to **learn** something new.

You might dare yourself to **stop a bad habit**.

You might dare yourself to **add something healthy** or positive to your **daily routine**.

PUSH YOURSELF!

Finish the sentences below with a dare or two for yourself:

I dare myself to _drink eight glasses of water every day._

I dare myself to _____.

I dare myself to _____.

I dare myself to _____.

I dare myself to _____.

Something to remember—CONFIDENCE IS CONTAGIOUS!

The more **confident** you feel in yourself and your abilities, the more confident **others** will be in your abilities too!

BE CONFIDENT IN YOURSELF—AND SPREAD IT AROUND! I dare you!

PART 3

SKILLS VERSUS TALENT

> Talent you have naturally. Skill is only developed by hours and hours and hours of beating on your craft.
>
> — **Will Smith, American actor and rap artist**

ARE YOU READY FOR ME TO DROP SOME MAJOR KNOWLEDGE?

Time to talk about your TALENTS and SKILLS. There is actually a big difference between them. Is your mind blown yet?

Let's make it clearer.

Talent is something you're **born with**. It's your **natural ability** to be good at something without really being taught. You can usually be pretty good at a talent without really thinking about it. Examples of talents might be singing or being able to run really fast without even practicing. Even though you may be born with a certain talent, you can always **work to improve your skills** and **become better** at that talent.

Skills, on the other hand, are things you may **have to work a little harder to develop.** A skill is an ability to do an activity or job well, especially through **practice**. Skills are usually developed through lots and lots of hard work. Don't worry, hard work is a good thing!

You can, and do, have both talents and skills!

The awesome thing about a skill is that **it is always within your reach to accomplish.** You have the power to do something new, and to be exceptional at it. Remember, PRACTICE and HARD WORK is all it takes.

IF YOU HAVE NATURAL TALENT IN A CERTAIN AREA AND YOU SUPPORT THAT TALENT WITH LOTS OF PRACTICE, CHANCES ARE IT WILL BE QUICKER AND EASIER FOR YOU TO IMPROVE. YOU MAY JUST BECOME AN EXPERT SOMEDAY!

Let's look at the example of **Sarah** and **Taylor**. They are both 10 years old and they are both **naturally talented in sports**, especially running.

Sarah enjoys running from time to time at recess and has always been the fastest in her class (even faster than the boys—go, Sarah!). Recess is about the only time that Sarah ever runs.

who do you think will have more success with running, Sarah or Taylor? why?

Taylor joined the school track team and always makes sure to practice several times a week. She used to be the fifth fastest in her grade, but she's now the second fastest in the whole school (including the older kids—go, Taylor!). She has plans to join the county track team and even has dreams of competing in national competitions in the future.

- What are some **natural talents that you have?** Are there some things you've just always been able to do?

- How about skills? What are some things that you've really **had to work hard to learn** or master?

Tree of Talents and Rainbow of Skills

Meet the Tree of Talents and Rainbow of Skills! Take a moment to fill in the **tree with your unique talents** and the **rainbow below with any special skills** you may have. And just in case you've forgotten—you are every bit as beautiful as this tree and this rainbow.

It is super-important to remember that **just because you may not have been born with a certain talent, like a natural ability to paint, it doesn't mean you can't do it.** You may just have to work a little harder than someone who was born with the natural ability to paint.

> You are capable of mastering whatever skills and talents you want. The sky's the limit!

And you can be whatever you want, Girl!

LET'S TAKE A LOOK AT KIERA'S STORY.

Kiera is 10 years old. She loves to **sing** and play the **piano**. Her parents are also very good singers. Kiera was able to sing before she could even talk. When she was only five years old, she was already singing in local plays and winning talent shows. Singing has always just come easily to Kiera, and she is very good at it. But Kiera knows that even though she has a natural talent, she still has to practice and take lessons if she wants to be a really big success.

Having a talent won't make her the best unless she works on it.

Kiera also enjoys playing **the piano**, but it's been **harder** for her than singing. She started taking lessons when she was six years old. She had to practice five days a week, every week, to learn to play. Because Kiera has been taking lessons for several years and sticking to her practice routine, she has finally learned to play the piano very well and can play many of her favorite songs. Kiera knows she'll need to continue practicing to keep developing her skill. Through hard work and practice, not only does Kiera improve, but she also **feels pretty good about herself!**

The Piano of Achievements

Let's have another exercise! Take a look at the keys of a piano. On each key, I want you to write one word that describes how you feel when you work hard to achieve something. I've done the first one for you.

Excited

> A WINNER IS SOMEONE WHO RECOGNIZES HIS GOD-GIVEN TALENTS, WORKS HIS TAIL OFF TO DEVELOP THEM INTO SKILLS, AND USES THESE SKILLS TO ACCOMPLISH HIS GOALS.
>
> — *Larry Bird, former basketball player for the Boston Celtics*

Your talents and your skills

Choose **one talent** that you have and **one skill** that you want to develop and improve:

A natural talent I have

A skill I want to develop

You can look back at your Tree of Talents and Rainbow of Skills to help.

What do you want to do in the future? What are your hopes and dreams for your skills and talents? Think BIG!

Part 4

WHAT IT TAKES TO BE SUCCESSFUL

> We can choose challenge, or we can choose comfort. But we can't have both. Not at the same time.
>
> — *Brene Brown, American author and professor*

WHAT IS A SUCCESS?

Let's talk for a minute about **success**. Of course, we think of success as being sparkly and shiny and amazing.

Simone Biles, an American gymnast, has had a hugely successful career! At the young age of 24, she has a combined total of 32 Olympic and World Championship medals, making her the most-decorated gymnast of her generation.

Greta Thunberg was wildly famous by the age of 15 for her thoughts and actions around climate change. By 18, the world-renowned environmental activist from Sweden had already won a number of prestigious honors and awards, including two nominations for the Nobel Peace Prize.

Kamala Harris is the first woman to clinch a vice presidency in the United States. The highlights of her career include time as state senator, attorney general, and district attorney. She is currently the highest-ranking female official in US history.

These are all successful women who had dreams, big dreams! Through lots of **hard work, planning, and preparation, they achieved those dreams**. Now all three of them are known around the world for their successes.

But ... does being successful mean being FAMOUS? **Not at all**.

What does it really mean to be successful? In the simplest terms, it means **you did what you set out to do**.

IT MEANS YOU SET A GOAL, AND YOU WERE ABLE TO ACHIEVE IT.

A goal could be really BIG and long-term, like being an Olympic champion or a president. It could also be small but important things in your daily life, like learning the basics of gymnastics.

You know what they say—every journey **starts with a single step**, and **small steps** lead to **BIG CHANGES**!

Do you have a BIG DREAM or a long-term goal?

Would you love to change something small but important in your life?

Think about it like this—maybe you got a C- on your last math test. It's your goal to raise your score at least one grade on the next test. So you study and study and study—and you get an A-! Congrats! You've met the expectation you set for yourself! You've succeeded!

So are **only big accomplishments** like grades considered successes? Absolutely **not**! Maybe you want to hit the snooze button one less time on your alarm clock so you aren't rushing around like crazy in the morning. You get up five minutes earlier one morning. Boom! **Success!** Success comes in all shapes and sizes.

This small achievement can lead to a bigger goal! Your dreams can come true. You can do it!

Now, are you ready for the next step? I am so excited to share my 10 secrets with you!

10 SECRETS TO HELP YOU BE WHATEVER YOU WANT!

These are SUPER-IMPORTANT RULES and HELPFUL TIPS to help you

SUCCEED AT WHATEVER IT IS YOU WANT TO DO.

Some things may work better for you than others. Some may work better for your specific goal.

TRY THEM.

See what works for you and what helps you to be most successful in achieving your dreams.

1. IF YOU BELIEVE, YOU CAN ACHIEVE!

The first step toward being successful at anything is **believing in your abilities and believing in yourself.**

And, by the way, you should believe in yourself!

BELIEVE THAT YOU CAN BE WHATEVER YOU WANT, GIRL!

Start by telling yourself, either in **your head** or **out loud, I CAN DO THIS! I can be whatever I want!** This tip might sound a little silly or strange—but it works, and it can help you!

I will do this.
I will be successful.
I can do this. I will do this.
I will be successful.
I can DO whatever I want.
I can BE whatever I want.

Repeat this as many times as you need to. Make sure you really mean it! **The words we use can change our belief** systems and feelings. **Words create reality!** Try it!

Start by writing it here. Now.

Looks great! I do want to warn you that this doesn't happen overnight. In order for this to really work, you are going to want to practice POSITIVE SELF-TALK on **a daily basis**. That's right—every day! You are worth it! Promise yourself you will do this for the next several days. Or even months! Or even years! It will pay off in the end.

2. FOLLOW YOUR PASSIONS.

When we talk about passion, we are talking about things that **excite you!** The things that make you want to be a better person! The things that put goose bumps up and down your arms! Get it?

IT'S EASIER TO WORK HARD IN THE LONG-TERM AND SUCCEED AT SOMETHING WHEN YOU HAVE A PASSION FOR IT.

So, try to **go after things you feel very passionate about.** If you try to achieve something you don't really care about, chances are you won't get very far with it.

Let's say you have a passion for singing, or maybe science. That will make it easier to put your heart and soul into those things. You'll be more willing to do whatever it takes to succeed.

If all the other girls in your class plan to audition for the school play, but you don't really have a passion for acting, **don't audition just because the other girls are doing it**. Find the areas that YOU are passionate about and GO AFTER THEM. **You are sure to find much more success this way**!

Yes, passions are great, but **life isn't always about just our passions.** There may be things you want to accomplish that you don't feel quite that passionate about. It's important to be aware of those things too, so you can be prepared to deal with them when they come up, even though they may not be your favorite things—like math class.

The Heart of Passions

Take a second to really think about your passions in life:

> Think about the things you **love to do**.
>
> Think about the things that **make you happy**.
>
> Think about the things you **put above all else**.

These are your passions. These passions will help you achieve your successes.

Think about some important things you may have **less passion** for—things you'd prefer NOT TO DO. These are the things you usually postpone, or avoid doing altogether. **But even if you don't love these things, it doesn't mean they're not worth doing.**

MY PASSIONS

NOT SO PASSIONATE ABOUT

3. STEP OUT OF YOUR COMFORT ZONE. DARE YOURSELF!

DON'T BE AFRAID TO DARE YOURSELF TO STEP OUT OF YOUR COMFORT ZONE.

Do you know what a comfort zone is? It's actually a good thing. It's a spot where you feel really comfortable and confident.

If you are used to **hanging out with your bestie** every day—this is your comfort zone. If you challenge yourself to make **a few more friends**—you are stepping out of your comfort zone.

If you're a shy girl and you prefer not to **participate in class discussions**—this is your comfort zone. If you dare yourself to **start joining the discussion**—you are stepping out of your comfort zone.

And getting out of your comfort zone means you are growing and developing into an even more amazing girl!

Your comfort zones

What are YOUR comfort zones—the spots where you feel really comfortable and confident?

_____

_____

_____

_____

_____

It's good to have comfort zones—and it's good to get away from your comfort zones sometimes too. Thomas Jefferson, the third president of the United States of America, once said:

"With great risk, comes great reward."

What in the world does that mean? It means that if you take yourself up on that dare to step outside your comfort zone, **it can have a huge payoff in the end**!

A dare can open you up to **NEW OPPORTUNITIES**. It can **empower you** to push yourself. It can **open your mind** to a whole new way of thinking. In other words, a dare can **lead to total success!**

Is there something you want to do, but maybe you've been a little nervous to try? Maybe it seems intimidating or feels a bit uncomfortable? Take a minute to jot down a few thoughts about this.

4. SET GOALS.

If you want to be successful, you have to be clear about what goals you want to achieve. There are lots of different types of goals.

You may set a goal to **learn something new**—like learning how to juggle.

You may set a goal to take on a **new challenge**—like making your bed every day for a week.

You may set a goal to **eliminate a bad habit**—like not biting your fingernails.

You may set a goal to **start a healthy practice**—like going to bed earlier.

YOU GET THE IDEA, RIGHT?

It's important to start by setting SMALL GOALS. If you start by setting huge, challenging goals, it can be hard to feel you're making any progress at all. This could lead you to giving up completely. And that's the last thing you want to do!

> ALWAYS REMEMBER, YOU HAVE WITHIN YOU THE STRENGTH, THE PATIENCE, AND THE PASSION TO REACH FOR THE STARS TO CHANGE THE WORLD.
>
> *— Harriet Tubman, American abolitionist and political activist*

5. MAKE PLANS.

After you've set your goal, you need to **come up with a plan**. The plan can be as detailed or as loose as you like—just think ahead.

What **steps** will you take to reach your goal? What will you do **first**? What things will you need to **achieve** your goal? **Putting it down on paper** can make your goal seem less overwhelming and more reachable.

We'll take a closer look at this in a bit too. I even have a special tool to help you make a great—and effective—plan. Stay tuned!

6. WORK HARD AND DON'T GIVE UP.

Nobody ever achieved anything without a little hard work. Remember Kiera and her singing talent? **Even the most talented people can't reach their goals without working hard.** Ask any successful person— famous or not. You can't do it without hard work.

WILL IT BE HARD? PROBABLY. IS IT WORTH IT? ABSOLUTELY!

Remember, **it doesn't happen overnight**. You have to remain CONSISTENT and DETERMINED in your efforts. And don't give up! Sometimes it can be tempting to just quit when things get too hard or you feel frustrated. Don't!

When you think you can't do it anymore, think about **the future**. How will success feel? How proud will you be when you've achieved your goal? The challenges you face in the moment are just **temporary obstacles**. You can do it, Girl! You can face it! Once you've overcome it, you will feel so **empowered**!

The Board of Negative and Positive Words

I want you to try something for me, okay? There are lots of different words on the board.

Some of the words are negative. They describe how you may feel when you want to give up. Some of the words are positive. They describe how you feel when you work hard and overcome that feeling of wanting to give up.

I want you to put a big black line through all the negative words. **Get rid of them!** Then I want you to circle all the positive words.

BRING ATTENTION TO THEM AND TAKE THEM WITH YOU ON YOUR JOURNEY!

proud   Strong   Empowered

    Unworthy   Weak

            Hopeless   Drained

~~Weak~~   (Hopeful) Exhausted   Happy

Tired   Overwhelmed

        Worthy

    Frustrated   Capable   Energized

Certain   Defeated

     Tough   Uncertain   Motivated

7. DON'T BE AFRAID TO MAKE MISTAKES.

HEY—DON'T BE AFRAID TO MAKE MISTAKES, GIRL!

I know this seems weird, but you can **gain so much from mistakes**—you just have to be willing to **learn from them.**

They can help to make you **smarter.**

They can help to make you more **creative.**

They can even help you become more **courageous.**

MISTAKES ARE A VERY GOOD THING, INDEED.

We'll talk a lot more about this later, and I'll show you an awesome tool you can use when things don't go exactly the way you planned.

8. BE FLEXIBLE.

You can set the most well-thought-out goals in the world and write the most detailed plans on the planet. Guess what? **Something unpredictable will probably happen.** So you need to stay flexible as you're setting and achieving goals.

Imagine you set a goal to run one mile on the school track every day after school. What happens if it rains? Or if the school is using the track? Stay flexible and go running in the gym or use the track after the school event. Don't give up! Find another way to do it!

You may have to **shuffle** timelines, resources, or expectations. It is so, so, so much easier to face these challenges if you are mentally and physically prepared for them. The strategies on the next page will go a long way toward helping you do just that!

- **Don't always expect everything to run smoothly.** As my grandma used to say: **"Expect the best, but plan for the worst!"**

- **Always have a Plan B.** Keep an extra tennis racket in your bag just in case the netting in your favorite one rips. Think ahead about what you'd do if you woke up late … Get the idea?

> Prepare yourself to be flexible, Girl!
> You can do it!

9. CELEBRATE YOUR SUCCESSES.

It's always fun to **celebrate**, and achieving a goal is tons of fun, right? Don't forget to acknowledge and celebrate **any progress** you make, **even if it's small**. You don't have to throw yourself a party for every little success you have. Celebration can look like sharing a proud moment with your family or best friend, or journaling about a victory you may have had that day.

Celebrate **not only the final achievement**, but also the PROCESS of getting there. Whoop-whoop!

Balloons of Successes

Can you think of ways to celebrate your success? Write one way to celebrate in each of the balloons below! When the time comes—and it will come—look back at these balloons and celebrate!

Share my success with my bestie Nia.

38

10. BE GRATEFUL AND THANK THOSE WHO HELP YOU ON YOUR PATH TO SUCCESS.

You should **never take for granted** all the cheerleaders you have as you work toward your goal. It can mean a lot of time and energy for someone to support YOU.

BE THANKFUL TO PEOPLE WHO GIVE YOU FEEDBACK, ADVICE, AND ENCOURAGEMENT.

Make sure they know they are **appreciated** and that **you value** what they did. It's great to tell them "THANK YOU," but it's even better to find unique ways to reward their kindness and generosity. Like the time my brother, Imri, was super-supportive in helping me study for a HUGE biology test. He gave me a little quiz using all my notes. I know that Imri loves chocolate, so I picked up a candy bar for him on my way home from school—after I aced my test!

 If you show you are truly appreciative, you'll find that **more people will be there for you!**

Just like I showed Imri I was appreciative, think about a few ways to show the people who support you how much you really appreciate their help. Better yet, ask them **what you can do for them!** (I guess sometimes people will just be polite and say something like "You don't have to do anything for me," but believe me, everybody appreciates some recognition. So for that person, take the initiative and come up with a surprise to thank them!)

My Appreciation Bank of Ideas

I want you to do this next activity with the **people who support you**. Find out how they like to be shown appreciation. Ask specific questions about the things they like. Maybe it's a small gift—like Imri's candy bar. Maybe it's kind words, or a card, or even a hug. Only they will be able to tell you. Write the name of one person who supports and encourages you on the ribbon of each of the gifts below. Write how they like to be appreciated on the gift.

Part 5

YOUR LEARNING RESOURCES

> **Do what you love and the necessary resources will follow.**
>
> — *Peter McWilliams, American author*

Now that I've shared my 10 secrets for success, I need to tell you about another important part of this journey—something else that's essential to your success. In fact, it would be pretty tough for you to get very far without it. It's called **RESOURCES**! On your path to success, you're going to need **RESOURCES**.

WHAT DO YOU MEAN "RESOURCE"?

A resource can be materials, tools, time, money, or even other people—anything that can **support you in reaching your goals**. Resources have lots of different purposes. They can be used to support you in many ways.

A RUNNER NEEDS ...

a good pair of shoes to support her feet.

a coach to guide and motivate.

a sports app to track distance and speed.

internet to look at research and scientific studies.

support from her family to cheer her on.

A SCIENTIST NEEDS ...

- a lab to work in.
- a computer for recording observations.
- a library for research.
- a senior professor to learn from.
- time to learn and spend in the lab.

A 10-YEAR-OLD GIRL WHO WANTS TO BE ON TIME FOR SCHOOL—RATHER THAN LATE AS USUAL—NEEDS ...

- a good alarm to wake her up.
- a parent to help her set up a good schedule.
- a teacher to be understanding and supportive.

I think you get the picture...

Do you know that you have resources available to you too? There are lots of **tools**, **materials**, experiences, and people that can help you reach your goals and achieve your dreams.

So how does all this apply to your wish to be successful? We've already agreed that if you want to succeed you need to have a clear GOAL. And then you need to create a PLAN to help you achieve your goal. But it's tough to create your plan and achieve your goal if you don't have RESOURCES for LEARNING AND GROWTH.

 RESOURCES will help you gain the **knowledge** and **experience** you need to reach your goal.

There are plenty of RESOURCES in the world. And the good news is lots of them are **FREE** and **AVAILABLE** whenever you need **them! You just need to choose wisely.**

There are tons of **online resources** out there.

You can learn a lot from **books and magazines**.

Software and apps are another amazing tool that's right at your fingertips.

Time is a precious resource for any goal you set. If you manage your time wisely, you will have more time to learn and practice.

And one of the most important resources you can use is actually other **people**.

By learning from the experiences of others, you can get different perspectives to help you reach your goals. You can use all different types of people as a resource—people with hands-on **experience**, **experts** in their field, or just **supportive** and **kind people** who will encourage you when you run into challenges.

 These are all fantastic tools to help you along the way. Remember, **choose your resources wisely and make the most of them.**

One key to success is to develop a **WIDE COLLECTION OF RESOURCES**. This is important because resources aren't usually "one-size-fits-all"— which means the same resource won't work in every situation. You may need different resources to help you reach different goals in different situations.

And here is a secret resource I can share with you. A resource that YOU can create for yourself to help with each and every goal you set. Are you ready?

MEET THE "I DARE MYSELF" NOTEBOOK

Start **A NEW NOTEBOOK** for any goal or plan you set. A fresh notebook, **dedicated to a specific goal**, is perfect for writing your thoughts, insights, and ideas. It's also a great place to keep track of research and new learning. And whenever I start a new notebook to help me reach a goal, I always go back to the concept of daring myself. I call it the "I DARE MYSELF TO ... notebook!"

Later I'll show you my *I DARE MYSELF TO BE ELECTED SEVENTH-GRADE CLASS PRESIDENT notebook!*

And my *I DARE MYSELF TO BE A SUCCESSFUL AUTHOR notebook.*

I just love how that sounds, don't you?

Now let's look at a few important resources you might use to help you achieve your goal.

ONLINE RESEARCH

The **internet** is one **huge learning resource!** You can find videos, online courses, and group discussions or forums. All you have to do is to log onto a computer or your mobile device. Name any subject in the world and you'll find dozens of **photos, articles, blogs, vlogs,** and helpful **videos** to inform and inspire you. Not to mention the thousands of **articles** and **eBooks** that are also available online. There's so much information out there!

Here are few tips that may be helpful:

1 Bookmark important sites on your computer or mobile device. If you find it easier, you can just **jot down the site addresses** in your I DARE MYSELF notebook or your mobile device. Just make sure you keep track of the really important stuff so you can go back to those sites as many times as you need to.

2 Open a file and **paste any relevant pieces of** information you gather along the way. Make sure to save it to your computer so you can easily find it.

BOOKS, MAGAZINES, AND OTHER MEDIA

Online resources are great, but the **traditional** route can be helpful and inspiring too.

The library is a great place to spend an afternoon. You can find up-to-date information and also be inspired by the history and knowledge around you. Books, magazines, and newspapers cover just about every subject in the world.

Most libraries use **organizational systems** that group all the books on the same topic together. You can find shelves full of books to help you reach any goal, whether it's learning how to make the perfect loaf of bread or strengthening your body through weight training.

There are tons of different kinds of **magazines and newspapers** out there, ranging from fun and light-hearted to seriously informative. You can find magazines about almost **every topic in the world**! Sports, science, fashion, food and cooking, automobiles, hobbies and crafts ... you name it! Maybe your local library doesn't have every magazine in the world (they probably don't), but if you're looking for a more specific topic, there's a good chance **a librarian can point you** in the right direction. Make sure to pay attention to **publication dates** so you get the most current information possible.

And don't hesitate to go to the **librarians** with any questions you may have. They can help you to find information of any kind.

SOFTWARE AND APPS

There's plenty of software and mobile apps that can be **handy resources for almost anything**! They're designed to be **user-friendly**, meaning they often provide tutorials or break things down into simple, step-by-step directions. All you have to do is open up your laptop or mobile device—and then open up your mind!

Software or mobile apps can be helpful in a lot of ways. They go way beyond just helping you learn new things. They can give you all sorts of important **tools** like timers, trackers, calendars, calculators, logs—whatever!

> There are apps for literally everything. There are even apps to help you calm down, take a deep breath, and focus on your goal.

And finding the right app is super-easy! Just open the **Play Store** or **App Store** on your cell phone and search for an app that can help you. You'll be surprised at how many answers and tools you'll be able to find!

> ## WE TEND TO BECOME LIKE THOSE WE ADMIRE.
> — *Thomas Monson, American religious leader*

MENTORS

Pop Quiz!

? What do the following people have in common: big sisters, teachers, and coaches? Answer!

! They can all play the part of mentor to you. Yes, you!

A mentor? What's that? A mentor is someone who **influences** you, someone who can **guide** you and give you direction as you are setting and achieving goals. A mentor is someone you **trust**, someone who'll give you **honest advice**, and someone who's always **rooting for you** (just like me!). If you haven't already figured it out, a mentor can play a pretty important role in **helping you achieve your goals**.

A mentor doesn't have to be just a teacher or a sibling or a coach. Lots of different people could fill the role of mentor for you. This should be a special relationship, unique to you and the specific goals that you have set for yourself. **Is there anyone you can think of who might be an awesome mentor for you?**

Part of the job of a mentor is to **help you fly high and support you as you reach your goals!** As you can see, there are three high-flying kites below. Each kite describes an important aspect of finding and using a mentor. Check out the kites, and then think about how you would like to use a mentor to help you fly high!

Finding a Mentor

Why is this important?

Mentors can encourage and empower you to grow and develop. They can also help connect you to other resources and people to help achieve your goals.

Ways to do this

Find someone whose life path matches up to your goals. Talk with this person. Ask them questions about their choices. Ask them if they'd be willing to help you.

Whoever you choose as a mentor will likely already have experience in whatever it is you want to accomplish. They'll have the knowledge and experience to point you in the right direction.

Seeking Advice from a Mentor

Why is this important?

Ways to do this

Clearly describe your goals and the kind of guidance and advice you need. This is the only way your mentor can figure out how best to help you succeed.

Getting Feedback from a Mentor

Why is this important?

Mentors provide honest feedback in a way that helps build you up and inspires you to improve, rather than making you feel weak and defeated.

Ways to do this

You have to be open to your mentor's feedback and willing to make the changes your mentor suggests. Understand that they're not trying to make you feel bad—just trying to help you succeed in what you want to do. If you take their feedback seriously, you will succeed. Got it? Good!

ROLE MODELS

Mentors are super-helpful to have around, but there are other people who can be just as helpful. One of your resources might be a **role model**. A role model can be anyone you **connect** with and **admire**—maybe a sports figure, an author, or an influencer in the area you're interested in.

You may **not necessarily know** your role model personally, but **you look up to their ideas** and **accomplishments**. Unfortunately, you usually won't have personal access to a role model in the same way you may have access to a mentor, but you can still **learn a lot about them** and BE INSPIRED BY WHAT THEY DO AND HOW THEY DO IT!

There are actually two different kinds of books that can help you learn about your role model's life.

→ **A biography** is a book about someone's life written by another person.

→ **An autobiography** is a book about someone's life written by that person.

When you think about successful people, think about someone that inspires you! Learn from them, gather ideas, and be motivated! Try it, Girl!

> ## PEOPLE WHO DREAM OF SOMETHING BIGGER AND BETTER ARE GOOD ROLE MODELS.
>
> — *Andrew Shue, American actor*

Who's Your Role Model

Like we talked about earlier, every successful person needs to have someone to look up to. It could be a famous person you admire. It could be a leader in your community. It could even be someone in your family or close circle of friends.

Take a quick second to answer the questions below.

A. Who are **three successful people** that inspire you? Choose at least one woman. This could either be someone you know personally, or someone you admire from afar, like a celebrity or an author.

_____

_____

_____

B. Why do each of these people inspire you?

_____

_____

_____

_____

C. How can you **learn about these people**? What resources can help you?

_____

_____

_____

_____

D. What is a quality one of these people has that **you would also like to have**?

_____

_____

_____

_____

Do a little research

If you really want to know more about your role model and how THEY became whatever they wanted—if you want to learn about all their great accomplishments and HOW THEY MADE IT—you're going to **have to dive a lot deeper**! That deep dive starts with research.

An excellent way to begin is by **interviewing** your role model (if it's someone you know personally). Ask them ALL THE QUESTIONS in the world! Their answers should help you navigate your path to success.

If you don't know your role model personally, it's time to practice your research skills.

It's a lot easier than it sounds. In fact, you'll probably find researching your role model really inspires you!
Take advantage of this!
So, how do you get started?
Easy!

→ List your questions

Start by preparing a list of questions. The questions should cover anything and **everything you ever wanted to know** about your role model. Use your I DARE MYSELF notebook, or save your questions as a file in your electronic device.

You can use some of my questions below, or add a few of your own:

- What natural talents does my role model have?
- What are the skills my role model has developed over time?
- What qualities make my role model successful?
- When and how did my role model make their big breakthrough? How did this lead them to being successful in what they do?
- What failures have they had along the way and how did they learn from them?
- What helpful tips, recommendations, and important messages might they have for others?
- What qualities can I adopt from my role model now, even though I'm young?
- What are ways I can be like my role model later on, when I'm grown up?

→ Search and use any learning resource you know.

Now that you have your questions figured out, you can use ANY LEARNING RESOURCE in your collection to find your answers. (Hint: Go back to the beginning of this chapter if you need a quick resource review.)

You can find answers online by searching for **interviews** with your role model or **reading articles** about them. You may even be able to find **articles** or **books** that they wrote themselves. Look for any and all **publications** about your role model.

→ Gather all pieces of information.

Capture every RELEVANT or INTERESTING piece of information—piece-by-piece, step-by-step.

→ Rearrange the information to get clear answers.

Once you've scoured every resource for pieces of information, it's time to start putting it all together. **Review and organize** the information in a way that makes sense to you. This will help you answer your questions and provide guidance in reaching your goal!

There you go! You did it! Congratulations!

And Girl ... you can research ANYTHING you want or ANYTHING you need! Research is an extremely POWERFUL tool to use in all sorts of situations. It can help you **learn something new**. It can help you **make decisions**. It can help you to **find an answer**. It can **introduce you to a new subject**. Or it can just help to **inspire and energize you**!

ADVICE AND FEEDBACK

We've talked a bit about seeking advice and feedback from your mentor, but other people may be able to give you good ideas too, even if they're not specifically your mentor.

whatever you decide to do, make sure it makes you happy.

Imagine that you've set a goal to help your basketball team win the state championship. Your basketball coach may not have the time to be a mentor to you, but she's still available for guidance and advice. Use it to learn!

Ask for informal advice, or hang out for a couple of extra minutes after basketball practice to ask her **how she thinks you're doing** and **how you might be able to improve**. You can reach out for feedback and a little advice from all sorts of people. Think about someone who has already accomplished what you want to accomplish.

→ Ask for feedback. Don't wait, Girl!

> Don't be shy! Go! Seek people out and ask questions. Ask for feedback!

And don't expect someone to openly share feedback and advice without being asked. **Most people won't.** They may think you're not interested in what they have to say, or they may not want to make you feel uncomfortable. So … **ASK them.** Chances are, once people understand that you're open to feedback, most will be happy to help.

They'll also be more willing to offer advice and more SUPPORT in the future.

You can get informal feedback from **anyone**. It doesn't have to be an expert! It can just be someone you're comfortable bouncing ideas back and forth with. Of course, it doesn't hurt to seek advice from someone with experience in your area of interest too.

→ Feedback and advice can be tough to hear.

Oh, yes! Let's face it, Girl! Getting feedback can **sometimes feel a little embarrassing, or even insulting**. It can be tough to admit there may be room for improvement. But there always is. The sooner you accept that fact, the sooner you can put the good feedback to work!

The same is true for getting advice. It can feel strange. You might think it won't help to take advice, or that it will be too hard—or even impossible—to follow.

BUT REMEMBER THIS

> If it's tough to get advice or feedback in a certain area, chances are **this may be the area where you need that advice and feedback THE MOST.**

Don't **reject** advice just because you assume **it can't help you**. Think about **what you can take from it**. Think about **why** the person thought it was a good idea to share it with you. Hopefully the people who are giving advice have your best interests at heart, but even so, you're the only one who knows what's right for you.

Don't **be hurt by the feedback or advice you receive**. Yes, sometimes in the first moments it may feel a little discouraging. That's natural. It happens to everyone!

Challenge yourself to **wait a few minutes**, or even to **sleep on it**. Then start to seriously think about **what you can learn** from this feedback or advice. How will this help you **grow** into an even **more amazing girl**!

> " AVERAGE PLAYERS WANT TO BE LEFT ALONE. GOOD PLAYERS WANT TO BE COACHED. GREAT PLAYERS WANT TO BE TOLD THE TRUTH. "
>
> — *Doc Rivers, American basketball coach*

Now, what to do with all this feedback and advice?

It's not enough to just receive the feedback. You have to make sure you **learn and grow from it.**

Remember your I DARE MYSELF notebook?

It can help to **write down any advice or feedback** that strikes you as valuable.

I DARE MYSELF TO BE
ELECTED
7th GRADE
CLASS PRESIDENT

Then you can revisit it and write down any **progress you've made**.

Be sure to update the person who gave you the feedback too.

Let them know how you're doing, and ask if they have any more advice for your "**next steps**."

Let's make a list of the people you think might be able to provide you with valuable feedback and advice. Choose an area where you want to improve, and then think about people who can supply you with good advice and honest feedback in this area. I added one of mine at the top of the list.

Area in my life where I want to be more amazing	The right people to give me advice or feedback
Get over my fear of speaking in front of an audience.	- My Aunt Jodie, who is a college professor. - Dani, a girl from my class who used to struggle with public speaking but overcame it.

Who is someone you could go to for informal advice and feedback?
Remember, this person is not your mentor or your role model.

CIRCLES OF SUPPORT

If you want to succeed, it's a good idea to surround yourself with friends and others who force you to **level up**. Find people who have a desire to learn and grow, just like you!

It's beyond important to **STAY AWAY FROM NEGATIVE PEOPLE**! Don't waste your time on people who tell you that it's not worth trying, or it's best to just give up.

Seek out **POSITIVE PEOPLE** for support, advice, and feedback. I promise you—they are out there!

MAKE FRIENDS WHO MAKE YOU A BETTER PERSON.

Surround yourself with people who will **learn and grow together with you** and share in your journey to success!

Find support from people who **care about you and your success**. Friends and family members can be huge in helping you to be more amazing and meet your goals.

They may not always be able to point you in the right direction, in terms of specific information and steps to take, but they can be there to **encourage you**. These are the people who **pick you up when you fall down**, the people who **push you to keep going**, the people who want you to be **the VERY BEST YOU that you can be!**

This circle may just be the most important resource you can have!

Who is the first person you would turn to when you need help?

Don't forget to take a break if you need to. You have lots of time!

Circles of Support

Do you see the three circles below? Fill in each circle with someone you'd like to have in your Circle of Support. The inner circles are for the support people you're closest to, and the outer circles are for any others who support you. Who exactly are these people? A parent? A friend? Why are they part of your Circle of Support?

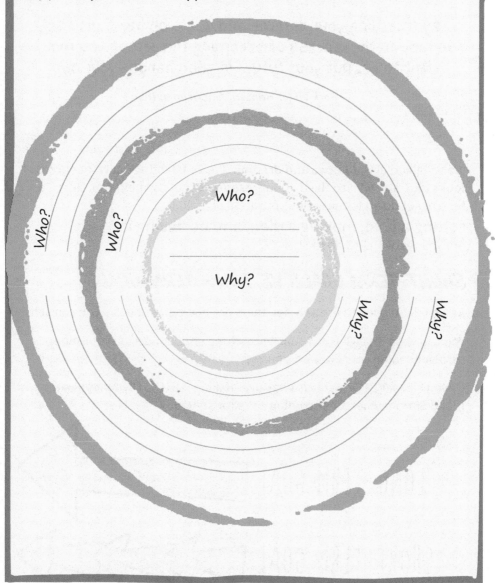

Who?

Who?

Who?

Why?

Why?

Why?

Part 6

SETTING AND ACHIEVING YOUR GOALS

> By recording your dreams and goals on paper, you set in motion the process of becoming the person you most want to be. Put your future in good hands—your own.
>
> — **Mark Victor Hansen, American author**

We've talked about **hopes and dreams**. We've talked about what **success looks like**, and we've talked about **resources** that can help you. Now it's time to get down to the serious business of actually

setting a goal, making a plan, and achieving it.

Are you ready? Let's do this!

SHORT-TERM GOALS VS. LONG-TERM GOALS

As we talked about a little earlier, there are two types of goals you can set.

You can set a SHORT-TERM goal, like getting good grades on your report card or keeping your closet organized.

Or you can set a LONG-TERM goal, like making it to the Olympics like our friend Simone Biles, or becoming a doctor someday.

LONG-TERM GOAL

SHORT-TERM GOAL

> The main difference between short-term goals and long-term goals is the TIMELINE for achieving the goal. SHORT-TERM goals can usually be reached in a few days, weeks, or months. LONG-TERM goals can take more time, even years, to achieve.

When setting a goal, you should include BOTH the long-term goal and the short-term goals that will get you there. Your short-term goals should help you reach a long-term goal. That means your long-term goals can, and should, be made up of many short-term goals and tasks.

Think of it like this. Maybe you set a long-term goal to go to an excellent college after high school. Your short-term goal would be getting good grades and seeking out the recommendations that will help you get into a good college—your long-term goal.

When setting goals, start with your long-term goal. That way you can figure out what short-term goals you're going to need to get to that long-term goal.

Think of your short-term goals as the INGREDIENTS that make up your long-term goal.

To set your long-term goal, it can help to start by figuring out just exactly what you want your future to look like. Think about two years from now, or even five or ten years from now—when you'll be a grown woman.

Where do you want to be?

What do you want to be doing?

Then think about what short-term goals you might need to get there. You can even set more than one long-term goal for yourself.

Let's do a little imagining. Close your eyes and take a deep breath. Imagine where you want to be in a year, or two years, or five years. Use these images and thoughts to help shape your plans. You can do this whenever you're making plans for the future, or even when you're facing a challenge. Ready, set, imagine!

I want to be

In _____ years, I want to _____

In _____ years, I want to _____

In _____ years, I want to _____

In _____ years, I want to _____

I'm going to share with you some goals I set for myself in the past, and then I'm going to **walk you through** exactly how I went about reaching those goals. You can use me as an example to help you figure out how to set your own goals.

When I was in sixth grade, I decided that I wanted to be elected president of the seventh-grade class. Even though the class election was almost a year away, I set my long-term goal early so I had plenty of time to achieve it.

The first thing I did was start my I DARE MYSELF notebook. On the very first page, in huge letters, I wrote:

I DARE MYSELF TO BE ELECTED SEVENTH-GRADE CLASS PRESIDENT.

This made my LONG-TERM goal ultra-clear!

The next thing I wrote in my I DARE MYSELF notebook were my SHORT-TERM goals. I gave myself six to nine months to achieve these goals:

1. *Get to know everyone in my class and make sure everyone knows me.*

2. *Learn how to run an effective campaign for class president.*

3. *Learn about and understand what the president does—what responsibilities they have—so I'll know what to do if I become president.*

I set three short-term goals to help me reach my long-term goal. Way to go, me!

Your short- and long-terms

What about you? Let's set your short-term and long-term goals.

Do you remember a little earlier when you imagined where you might be in one year or two years or even five years? Choose one of those situations. This is your LONG-TERM GOAL. Write it here one more time, just so you can be ultra-clear too.

Start with **I DARE MYSELF TO:**

Now, just like I did, try to think of a few short-term goals that can help you achieve this.

BREAKING DOWN THE SHORT-TERM GOALS INTO SMALLER, BITE-SIZED TASKS

☑ Long-term goals set? Check!

☑ Short-term goals set? Check!

After I set my goals, it was time for me to break down my short-term goals into **bite-sized little chunks**. I made a list of tasks to do for each short-term goal. When you do this, your SHORT-TERM GOALS seem a little more **simple to manage** and **easier to complete**.

1 How do you think I broke down my first **short-term goal: getting to know every kid in class?** I gave myself the task of having a **conversation with one kid every day over the next several weeks.** One kid seems a lot less intimidating than a whole class.

2 Let's look at my other short-term goals. How do you think I could have broken them down into even smaller, even more manageable parts? To learn how to **run a winning campaign**, one task I set was reaching out to an experienced person. I talked to the current seventh-grade president to find out how he got elected. To learn more about **what the president does**, one task I set was to watch a seventh-grade meeting.

When you think about tasks, it can also help to add **TIMELINES**. A timeline is kind of like a schedule of events with the order that you want them to be done. Timelines can be helpful because they give you a rough idea of when you **want to be finished** with something. It's really important to put a deadline on your timeline—the very latest date that a task can be completed. Deadlines can be **pretty motivating!**

Here's a list of my short-term goals and tasks:

Short-term #1 – Get to know everyone in my class.

Tasks:

- *Have a conversation with one kid every day over the next several weeks.*

Short-term #2 – Learn how to run a successful campaign for class president.

Tasks:

- *Schedule a meeting with the current or former seventh- and eighth-grade class presidents and interview them about the campaigns they ran.*
- *Prepare a list of questions about running campaigns to ask the current and former class presidents.*
- *Do online research about successful class-president campaigns.*
- *Check to see if there are any school guidelines for running an election campaign.*

Short-term #3 – Learn about and better understand the president's role and duties.

Tasks:

- *Learn from the current or former seventh- and eighth-grade class presidents.*
- *Find out how the president works with school committees.*
- *Research the school's guidelines for committees, how they work, and the purpose of each committee.*
- *Talk with one student from each committee.*
- *Volunteer on two school committees to understand how groups work together and support each other.*

Your turn. What tasks can you set to help you reach your short-term goals? Think about how you might break those goals down into a series of smaller things to do.

_____

_____

_____

_____

_____

WHAT ELSE DO YOU NEED TO ACHIEVE YOUR GOALS?
RESOURCES!

After I'd set my goals and tasks, it was time for me to go one step further and think about the **resources** I'd need for those short-term goals. Do you remember when we explored resources a little earlier? A resource could be a mentor, a book, an app, a website, or anything else that can help you reach your goals. We've already talked about how the **current seventh-grade president was a resource** for me. Here are some more resources I added to my list after I finished setting my tasks:

An app to help keep track of conversations with the kids from my class and keep important notes.

The current and former seventh- and eighth-grade class presidents – need to see if/how they can help me. Maybe one of them can be my mentor.

The school handbook – to learn about the rules for committee operations and the role of each committee.

A student who is active on one of the committees – to learn from their experience.

Online research – maybe I can learn from other schools about the class president's role.

Now think about yourself. What resources do you think you'll need to achieve the goals you've set for yourself?

_____

_____

_____

CHECK-INS AND FOLLOW-UPS

The last part of goal setting is all about **check-ins** and **follow-ups**. You'll need to check in on a very regular basis to make **sure you're on the right path** to make your dreams come true. You can use a check-in partner or check for yourself. And of course, you can also use both.

Adopt a check-in partner.

One of the most effective ways to make sure you're on the right path is to have a CHECK-IN PARTNER. This could be a friend, a family member, a teacher, a coach—anyone who **believes in you and wants to help you succeed**.

A check-in partner can help you **stay motivated** while reaching your goals.

They ask questions about your progress and **push you to keep going**.

Unlike a mentor, a check-in partner doesn't have to have a lot of experience or knowledge in the area of your goal. It can just be **someone who cares about you.**

Check Yourself.

You can also check in with yourself. Start by deciding **how often** to check in. Weekly? Every two weeks? Monthly? This can be different for every girl and every goal. Mark it in your calendar! That will help you remember to regularly look at your progress and make sure you're going in the right direction.

When you check in with yourself, don't forget to look at all the previous tasks you completed, while picturing your future success at the same time!

You can check in with yourself by **mentally reviewing** your progress or by keeping notes along the way. Reviewing something mentally means you think back through **all your hard work and progress in your head**. It can be quick and easy to do this when you have a few extra minutes on the bus or waiting in line. Of course, you can always use your I DARE MYSELF notebook to check in on your progress too.

It can be useful to **use both a check-in partner and self-checks** at the same time. Maybe you alternate between the two. Start with the self-checks, and then check in with your partner.

Gauge Your Status.

It's not enough to just check in, though. You also need to see where you are. That means you figure out **how satisfied you are with your progress**.

Are you doing what it takes to complete your short-term goals?
Are you moving along at a good pace?
If not, do you need to step it up?

This is where being flexible and making adjustments can come into play.

Let's take a look at the check-ins and follow-ups I used when achieving my goal. If you remember, one of my short-term goals was to **learn about the president's responsibilities**.

> This whole journal can be a helpful check-in tool for you as you reach your goals!

One of my tasks for achieving this goal was to join two school committees. I ended up choosing the fundraising committee and the after-school volunteer organization. I took my I DARE MYSELF notebook to each meeting. I used it to help me keep track of tasks and progress on my goals. During one check-in, I was going over my notes from the fundraising committee when I realized I had missed three out of the last five meetings. Also, the notes from the meetings I attended were patchy and disorganized. That check-in helped me understand that I could be making a little more progress with that task and goal.

What about you? What check-ins and follow-ups will you use?

MEET THE "MAKE-IT-HAPPEN" TOOL!

Here is an awesome tool to really help you plan out your goals. I call it the **Make-It-Happen** tool! You've already thought about a lot of things that go into making and achieving goals by reading about my experience.

Now it's time to **put it all together**. It's helpful to add specific details, like approximate dates.

Remember, we've talked about how it can be a good idea to have a few different goals with a few different timelines? Guess who else had a few different goals going? That's right! Me! Not only did I want to be seventh-grade class president, but I had, and still have, another dream. This goal is more long-term, something **I want to achieve as I develop into a smart young woman**. I want to be a **successful author!**

> In order to do that, I made another long-term plan (and of course, I have another notebook called I DARE MYSELF TO BE A SUCCESSFUL AUTHOR).

> I used this awesome tool to put my plan together. It's still in progress, but looking at it can help you learn how to use the Make-It-Happen tool for your own goals!

MAKE-IT-HAPPEN TOOL

MY LONG-TERM GOAL

I will be a successful author in 10 years,
with at least one published book.

MY SHORT-TERM GOALS	TASKS	CHECK-INS AND FOLLOW-UPS
1 Learn about the art and technique of good writing.	☆ Research creative writing course. ☆ Enroll in the course. ☆ Attend the course.	☐ Done ☐ Done ☐ I attended 7 out of 8 classes (missed for vacation). Final grade: B+
2 Learn about self-publishing.	☆ Research a few influencers/authors/bloggers on the subject of self-publishing. ☆ Read **The Art of Publishing.** ☆ Subscribe to a few self-publishing blogs and learn from them (take notes in my I DARE MYSELF notebook).	☐ My mom helped me with online research. I made a list of 3 authors and influencers. I'd like to add a few more later. ☐ Done. I made lots of notes to go over when I need them. ☐ One subscription done. Need to subscribe to a few more. I started to make notes. Need to do more ...
3 Practice my own writing and editing and get feedback.	☆ Create outline for short story. ☆ Write first draft. Share with mentor, family, and friend for feedback. ☆ Write final draft.	☐ Outline is half ready. Need to reorganize and show to my writing mentor. ☐ I wrote a few pieces of the story. I will continue once the outline is ready. I plan to share the full draft with my bestie Nia and one of the students from the online course I took. ☐ I will also compare the first draft and the final manuscript and analyze them to learn.

How's your energy level? Keep pushing! I'm right here with you!

4	*Publish my short story.*	⭐ *Research ways to publish my story.*	🔲 *I started to check online. Need to check with my English teacher and ask other people who might know.*
		⭐ *Make a list of different ways to publish my story.*	🔲 *I added a few ways to my I DARE MYSELF notebook. Need to add more.*
		⭐ *Send my story to sites and publishers who may be interested.*	🔲 *Need to prepare a list to keep track of where/who I sent my story to.*
5	*Write another new short story every 6 months.*	⭐ *Set timeline around outlining, writing, and submitting—planning months in advance.*	🔲 *I can use my notes app and calendar app to follow up and stick to my timelines.*
		⭐ *Share my stories with as many people as possible and gather feedback.*	🔲 *I made a partial list of people who would be interested in reading and giving feedback. Need to keep updating this list.*
6	*Write my first full novel.*	⭐ *Discuss writing a first novel with my writing mentor—and see if I need to get more knowledge and preparation for novel writing.*	🔲 *Better wait to start a novel till after I finish writing a few short stories.*
		⭐ *Make a plan and set timeline for writing a full novel. To start before getting to age 24.*	

HELPFUL RESOURCES FOR ACHIEVING MY GOALS

- *A diary/calendar app for setting dates.*
- *Writing mentor who can guide me and answer my questions – maybe my English teacher.*
- *Money to enroll in writing courses.*
- *Help from my mom to search for a writing course.*
- *Support from my friends and family to encourage me, read what I write, and make comments.*

Use the Make-It-Happen tool

Now that you are super-familiar with my goals, tasks, and follow-ups, it's time for you to give it a try!

MY LONG-TERM GOAL

MY SHORT-TERM GOALS	TASKS	CHECK-INS AND FOLLOW-UPS
1		
2		
3		

HELPFUL RESOURCES FOR ACHIEVING MY GOALS

_____

_____

_____

_____

_____

Take a breather if you need to. Then refocus and crush it!

A GOAL PROPERLY SET IS HALFWAY ACHIEVED.

— *Zig Ziglar, American author*

I've given you step-by-step instructions for setting your goals and making your plans. Now comes the exciting part! **It's time to get out there and start making it happen!** Keep this journal close by. There are so many important things in here, including your hopes and dreams! Good luck! **I know you can do it!**

P.S. I WAS elected president of the seventh-grade class!

Part 7

DEALING WITH CHALLENGES AND FAILURES

> Mistakes are proof that you are trying.
>
> — *Anonymous*

Have you ever heard of **Walt Disney**? What about **J. K. Rowling**? **Oprah Winfrey**? Of course, you've heard of all three. What do these three hugely successful people all have in common? Hang on to your socks for this one! All three faced major failures on their paths to success.

Walt Disney started out writing for a newspaper. His former editor and boss told him he **"lacked imagination and had no good ideas."** He went on to make **countless animated films** and create the "Happiest Place on Earth," **Disneyland**!

When **J. K. Rowling** first pitched the idea for Harry Potter, it was **rejected by 12 different publishers** before someone finally gave her a chance. She went on to write **seven best-seller Harry Potter novels**, which were later made into **mega-popular movies**.

And **Oprah Winfrey** was **fired from her first job as a news reporter**. Not only did she go on to host a **successful television show**, she even has her own magazine and an entire **television network**.

What if all three had given up after failing. Can you imagine? For starters, we'd have **no Mickey Mouse**, not to mention **no Harry Potter**!

Think about this: if these three successful people—and countless others—can pick themselves up after a major setback, don't you think that you can too?

It's important to go into any new venture **understanding that you might just make mistakes.** No big deal! Everyone makes mistakes, even Oprah Winfrey.

THE REAL MISTAKE WOULD BE NOT TRYING AGAIN.

Yes, it's really scary to try something new.

The first time you fail can be pretty scary too.

The next time you try, it might be a little less scary.

The next time you fail, it might be a little less scary.

With each new attempt, you'll gain more and more courage!

Do you want to know something else we wouldn't have if it wasn't for mistakes? **Post-it Notes.** That's right. Those colorful little sticky notes were created **by accident.**

In 1968, researcher Spencer Silver was charged with making a super-sticky glue—like, sticky enough to hold a space shuttle together. What he came up with instead was the slightly sticky, reusable glue that is used to make Post-its stick. Pretty awesome mistake!

1. Mistakes can help you remember that you are only human. They help you stay humble and understand that mistakes are just a part of life for everyone.

2. Mistakes can make you more creative. If what you are attempting to do isn't working, you open up your creative mind and look for another way to do it.

3. Mistakes can help you learn about yourself. They help you take a closer look at your strengths and your weaknesses. They help you understand that you may need support from others in areas that are challenging for you. Mistakes can also help you learn how to maximize your strengths.

4. Mistakes can lead to trying new things. Think of mistakes as a "wake-up call" for trying something new, learning something new, or experiencing something new that you wouldn't otherwise have experienced if it weren't for making mistakes.

> # BETTER TO DO SOMETHING IMPERFECTLY THAN TO DO NOTHING FLAWLESSLY.
>
> — *Anonymous*

DON'T IGNORE YOUR LESS SUCCESSFUL ATTEMPTS—ANALYZE THEM!

Have you ever heard anyone use the phrase **"sweep it under the rug"**? It's a figure of speech that means **rather than dealing** with something that is hard or uncomfortable, **you just hide it, ignore it, and forget about it.**

You definitely DO NOT want to sweep your mistakes under the rug!

 If you ignore your mistakes, **you're ignoring one of the best learning tools you have.** Remember those Post-it Notes? You'd be crazy to ignore all that good stuff!

PAY ATTENTION TO YOUR MISTAKES—PICK THEM APART!

Try to understand what caused you to make that mistake, and what you can do to keep from making the same mistake in the future. It's a little like squashing a bug. It might not be pretty to look at, but aren't you a little curious? (FYI, don't sweep a squashed bug under the rug either!)

And Girl ... not only should you accept that you're going to make mistakes, but you should be proud of all those little bumps in the road.

> # THE ONLY REAL MISTAKE IS THE ONE FROM WHICH WE LEARN NOTHING.
>
> — *Henry Ford, American industrialist and founder of the Ford Motor Company*

MEET THE "MAKE-IT-BETTER" TOOL
(YOUR LITTLE HELPER IN LEARNING FROM YOUR MISTAKES)!

Okay, we all agree that everyone makes mistakes. It's just part of the process, and it helps you to be a better you. So here's an awesome tool that can actually help you analyze what you did wrong and give you a few ideas about how you can do better next time. It's called the **MAKE-IT-BETTER** tool because that's just what it does—makes stuff better!

To use this tool, you'll need to start by thinking about **something you tried to do that didn't go well**, or maybe some stumbles you've had on the path to achieving your goal. I want you to really analyze what happened by answering the questions in the graph below.

Do you remember when I had a little problem with one of my short-term goals to **join two committees**? I actually used the Make-It-Better tool to help me figure out where I was going wrong, how I could fix it, and what I could learn from the situation. **Take a look at my mistake**—then think of a situation where you could use this tool to Make It Better! There's even a spot you can check once you've taken the steps toward making the situation better.

How are you doing?
Are you giving it your all?
Keep it up! ♡

MAKE-IT-BETTER TOOL

Description of the problem:
The other kids don't really listen to my ideas at the Fundraising Committee Meetings.

What went well

I signed up for the fundraising club and attended the first two meetings and gave two good ideas—a donut sale and an auction.

What went wrong

After the first two meetings, I missed the next three because I was really busy with other things. When I attended the next meeting, I had to use part of it to catch up on messages, which I did on my phone. I didn't think it really mattered ... When I tried to suggest an idea, no one listened to me. And they didn't like my other suggestions either.

What could have been done better

I could have been better about
- *Attending ALL the meetings.*
- *Being a more active part of the team.*

How I can make it better

- *Plan my schedule better to make sure I have time to attend meetings.*
- *Check on what topics were discussed at the meetings I missed and what topics will be discussed next.*
- *Prepare a list of ideas so I can be more prepared and able to contribute and have influence.*
- *Talk with others on the committee (maybe my friend Ruth) and get their perspective on my performance.*

Actions to take

- ☐ *Review, prioritize, and make changes in my schedule to make sure I have time to attend meetings.*
- ☐ *Ask my mentor for help with time management.*
- ☐ *Check for time-management videos online.*
- ☐ *Get ready for meetings in advance and come prepared with ideas.*
- ☐ *Find an app to help me capture notes and follow up on ideas.*
- ☐ *Take better notes in meetings and do follow-up.*
- ☐ *Put my phone aside so I won't be busy with it and can focus on the meeting.*
- ☐ *Be more active and engaged in the meetings I attend and provide ideas and feedback.*
- ☐ *Set reminders in my cell phone to review the notes and follow up on things.*
- ☐ *Set a time to talk with Ruth. Reflect on her feedback and advice.*

This tool is helpful in lots of ways—but the most important part is following up to make sure you've actually done all the things you said you were going to do to "make it better."

- Be sure to mark them off when you're finished—it'll feel great!
- You can also add due dates for every action. It can be very useful and motivating.

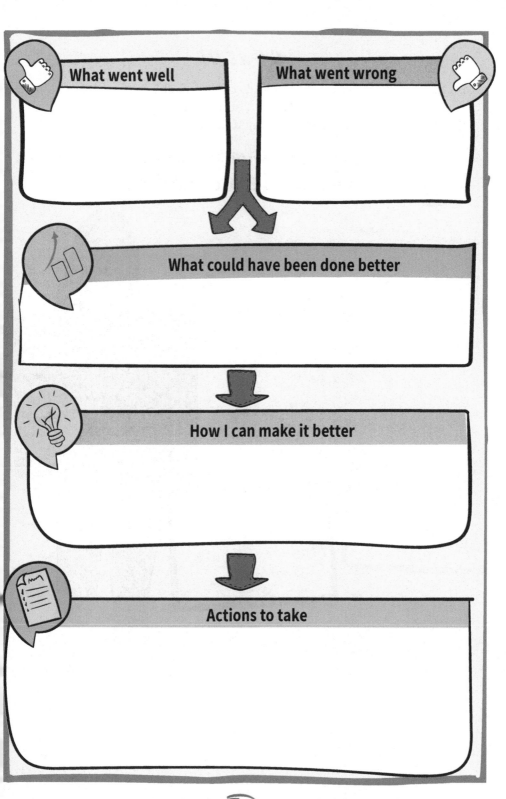

What went well

What went wrong

What could have been done better

How I can make it better

Actions to take

SHARE IT!

Do you want to know something really cool? Not only can you learn from your mistakes, but you can also learn from **other people's** mistakes, and other people **can learn from your mistakes.**

 Don't be afraid to have a **conversation about past failures**.

Talk about **what not** to do.

Talk about what you've learned.

Talk about how you tried again.

What do you need to succeed?

Check your resources—help is available!

Share your success and your failures.

Learn about the success and failures of those around you.

Have you ever heard anyone say, "It's no use crying over spilled milk"? That means that you shouldn't dwell on your mistakes.

JUST CLEAN THEM UP, MOVE FORWARD, AND DO BETTER NEXT TIME.

You see those two bottles of spilled milk? I want you to write one mistake you've made in the past on the first bottle, and what you've learned from the mistake in the puddle of milk. On the second bottle, I want you to write one mistake you've seen **someone else** make in the past, and what YOU learned from their mistake in the puddle of milk.

One more thing. We all make mistakes. **EVERY SINGLE ONE OF US!** Be quick to forgive yourself when you fail. Show yourself the same compassion you would show someone else if they messed up.

Do you remember when we talked about positive self-talk? You can use the same strategy to give yourself a little grace and forgiveness. The next time things don't turn out exactly as you expected, repeat one or more of the following phrases. Make sure you believe yourself when you say them!

I can learn.

I am not bad if I mess up.

WHEN I fail—I can grow.

Part 8

REFLECTION AND INSIGHTS

> *Reflection ... looking back so the view looking forward is clearer.*
>
> — *Anonymous*

You did it! You've put in so much thought about your **strengths** and your **goals**. You've learned all about **setting and achieving** your goals, and then you created some goals of your own. Maybe at this point, you've even taken the first steps toward achieving those goals.

Congratulations—and keep going, Girl!

We've already learned that self-reflection, or as we call it, **SelfRe,** is one of the most powerful tools a girl can use when moving toward success. It can help you achieve anything you want! **It's one of the keys to development and growth throughout life.**

The **more you SelfRe**, the **more opportunities** you will have to learn about yourself and all the different parts of your life.

The **more you learn**, the **more you grow**. This growth can help shorten your path to success!

DON'T KEEP IT TO YOURSELF. USE OTHER PEOPLE!

It can be a good idea to ask the people around you—friends and family—to reflect on exactly what **they see in you**. This can give you **a different perspective** about your thoughts and actions, a perspective you may not have been aware of.

We're all super-aware of some things about ourselves, but other things may not be so obvious. Asking for feedback from people might be the only way we can really **understand those less-obvious things**.

Let me share something with you ...

Remember when I joined the fundraising committee? So, for a really long time, I used to think that nobody listened to my ideas and suggestions at the meetings **because they weren't any good**. I even started to **doubt** if I was **smart enough** to be the next class president. I felt like this for weeks and weeks. The feeling just got bigger and more uncomfortable until it really started to **hurt my self-confidence**. I finally decided to ASK a friend on the committee, Ruth, what she thought about my ideas. Why did she think people weren't listening to my opinions?

Ruth was honest. She told me that **because I didn't attend all meetings** and **I was always messing around with my phone instead of listening to other people's ideas, no one really took me seriously.** She said I could have the most awesome ideas in the world and the other kids probably still wouldn't listen. If I'm not engaging with the other kids, then they won't engage with me.

WOW! That one hit me hard! **I was so surprised!** I would have never thought the others on the committee saw me that way. This short conversation with Ruth made A LOT of difference! It helped me understand that **it wasn't about my ideas**. It was about **MY ATTITUDE**. I probably would have never figured that out on my own.

I felt pretty embarrassed right after I talked with Ruth, but after thinking about it awhile, I felt really LUCKY that Ruth was so honest with me. Her feedback made a big difference in me.

If I hadn't talked to Ruth, I would have just kept thinking I wasn't smart enough. Instead, all I had to do was put the phone aside and start **listening to others**.

So, getting reflection from others can be great! But usually, the most important reflection is still Self-Reflection—SelfRe. Now, let's talk about WHEN you should SelfRe and HOW you can use it.

SelfRe is important as you examine every aspect of your life. You can SelfRe to process both the **small things** in life and the **BIG things** in life.

THE SMALL THINGS IN LIFE

SelfRe can be used for your **day-to-day** activities. Think about the things that happened earlier today, or yesterday, or even in the past few days.

You can reflect on how you interact with others:

- Do you sit back and listen most of the time, or do you do lots of sharing?

- Do you like to be right in the middle of the action, or do you prefer watching from the sidelines?

- Why do you think you respond this way?

You can reflect on how you spend your day:

- How much time do you spend being active?

- How much time do you spend relaxing?

- What do you do with your free time?

- Why do you prioritize your time in these ways?

You can reflect on the small decisions you make:

- What you chose for an after-school snack and why.

- What made you choose the apple over the bag of chips—or vice versa?

- What made you put off doing your homework?

Can you think of a time when you used SelfRe to make a choice or decision? I bet you can, Girl!

THE BIG THINGS IN LIFE

SelfRe is also incredibly important when you think about the **big things in your life**. In fact, you never want to make an important decision without putting TONS of thought into it through SelfRe.

Of course, when you set your long-term goals there is lots of SelfRe involved. And you should continue to SelfRe as you keep moving down the path to success.

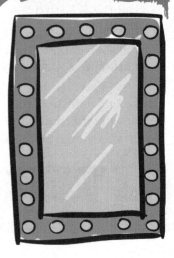

Reflect on the **past year**. In what areas did SelfRe help you make an **important decision** or **choice**?

Maybe the after-school activities you decided to be involved in? Maybe the kinds of people you chose to surround yourself with?

These are really big decisions that can affect your entire life. In what other BIG ways did you SelfRe?

I have another handy tool to help you SelfRe—and get feedback from others too!

MEET THE SELFRE BANK!

This bank is filled with lots of **SelfRe questions**. You can use these questions whenever it's time to do some reflection. Don't feel like you have to use all the questions every time. Pick and choose the ones that are the **most helpful to you in each unique situation**.

Anything worth doing is worth doing well.

Give it 100%!

SelfRe thoughts about yourself

- Do you like who you have become?
- What are your main strengths?
- What's your favorite thing about yourself?
- What would you like to change for the better in the future?

SelfRe thoughts about your emotions

- What excites you?
- What do you need to forgive yourself for?
- What makes you happy?
- What is one thing that caused you stress in the past week?
- What is one thing that filled you with joy in the past week?
- How do you handle anger and frustration?

SelfRe thoughts about relationships with others

- If someone else were to describe you, what do you think they'd say?
- How do you handle fights or disagreements?
- What is the nicest thing someone has ever said about you?

SelfRe thoughts about your learning and development

- What's a new skill you've learned recently?
- What is something you'd love to learn in the future?

SelfRe thoughts about your goals and your future

- What are your goals for next year?
- What big changes do you want to make in your life?
- What's the biggest challenge holding you back from achieving your goals?
- If you were to run into your school friends 10 years from now, how would you like them to view you?

Exploring these questions is just another way to **set yourself up for success**. If you have some idea what the road ahead of you may hold, you'll be far more prepared to travel that road.

" SELF-REFLECTION IS THE SCHOOL OF WISDOM.

— Baltasar Gracian, Spanish writer

Part 9

PAYING IT FORWARD

> When you learn, teach. When you get, give.
>
> — *Maya Angelou, American poet*

We've got one more really important area to cover. Let's talk a little about paying it forward. Throughout this book, I've poured information and inspiration into you. As you've set about achieving your goals, perhaps you've had people, such as role models or mentors, who've **helped you along the way**.

It's your turn to fill **someone else** with inspiration and knowledge. In this case, paying it forward means **being inspirational to someone else** just like someone inspired you.

That's right! Once you've achieved your goals, you can be the inspiration for someone else!

Pay it forward!!

Do this by being someone else's **cheerleader**.

Do this by being someone else's **listening ear**.

Do this by becoming someone else's **check-in partner**.

Do this by becoming someone else's **mentor**.

You can do this, Girl. PAY IT FORWARD!

Share the **information** you've gained from this journey and journal. Share the **knowledge** you learned from your mentor. Share the **compassion** and **encouragement** you received from your friends and family members. Just think, where would you be without **all that support**?

You couldn't have done it alone. You shouldn't let anyone else do it alone either. Especially now that you are kind of an expert!

Can you think of anyone you may be able to be an inspiration to— someone you could help become even more amazing? It can be a specific person, or a group—like younger classmates or teammates. Is there anyone in your life whose situation or goals might be similar to yours? If so, tell them how you can support them, and see if they want your help. (It's important to ask, because they may need a different kind of support than you've thought of. And then you get to decide what you can give.)

> When you give someone inspiration, it's like you are giving them a little ray of sunshine!

Pay-It-Forward Sunshine

Below, you will see three shining suns. In the middle of each sun, write **one person** you think you can "pay it forward" to. On each of the rays coming off the sun, write **one thing** you can do to pay it forward. I've done one for you.

Read lines with her to help her practice

My little sister, Dee, as she is trying out for the school musical

Attend the audition with her and cheer her on

Watch her routine for the audition and give her feedback

Take a breath and keep working through it.

> # FIND OUT WHO YOU ARE AND DO IT ON PURPOSE.
> — *Dolly Parton, American music artist*

A Letter to My Former Self

I have one more SelfRe exercise for you. I want you to write a letter to the **person you were before you completed this book**—the person you were before you met the goals you set for yourself. Maybe you've achieved some things that you didn't think you could achieve. Maybe you've overcome some fears you didn't think you could overcome. **Give that person some encouragement. Tell them how far they've come. Be your own inspiration!**

Dear Me,

_____

_____

_____

_____

_____

_____

_____

Now, I've got one last job for you to do. Look back at page 20 where you wrote the message in the bottle. I asked you to answer the following question:

> If you can be whatever you want, Girl—what do you want to be? What do you want to change?

Have you fulfilled that wish yet? Do you feel you have more tools and knowledge? If so—**congratulations!** If not—**that's okay, you can keep working on it,** using all the new tools and knowledge you now have to help you reach your dream. **Just don't give up!** You have time. **You can do it, girl!**

86

PART 10

LIRI'S TOP 10 TAKEAWAYS FOR YOU

> Many receive advice. Only the wise profit from it.
>
> — *Harper Lee, American novelist*

Advice ... I've given you a lot of that throughout this book. I want to make sure you keep all the most important pieces of advice at the front of your mind as you move forward in achieving your dreams. Are you ready for the **Top 10 Takeaways?** Here we go!

1. KNOW THE IMPORTANCE OF SELFRE.

When we use SelfRe, we are paying attention to our thoughts, our feelings, and the way we respond to others and the situations around us. **You can learn tons about yourself through SelfRe.** It can also help you set goals, make plans, and work through challenges. Just like I told you earlier, SelfRe is truly one of the most important tools a girl can use on the path to success.

2. BELIEVE IN YOURSELF.

All right, Girl, if you don't believe in yourself, no one else will either. Don't forget that! It can be challenging, and it might take a while, but there is no way around it. **You have to believe in yourself.** Remember, you will do INCREDIBLE things, and those incredible things start with a strong belief in yourself and your abilities.

3. DEVELOP YOUR SKILLS AND TALENTS.

There is a difference between skills and talents. While you may have been **born with a natural talent** for something, you have to **work harder to develop a skill**. One is not better than the other, and you can (and do) have both. Recognize your skills and recognize your talents, and do what you have to do to strengthen both so you can use them as you move forward toward success.

4. FOLLOW YOUR PASSIONS.

Figure out what it is that you truly love to do. Discover the things that are important to you. Decide exactly how you want to change the world. These are your passions! Chase them fiercely. I promise you'll have more success and a greater sense of purpose when you find your passions and follow them.

5. USE YOUR RESOURCES.

You have to take advantage of every resource around you. **Resources are a HUGE key to your success.** Books, articles, websites, libraries, newspapers, magazines, videos, role models, mentors—the list goes on and on. Because there are so many resources available, it shouldn't be too difficult to find the ones that work best for you. Discover them! Explore them! Use them every chance you get!

6. SET A GOAL AND MAKE A PLAN.

NOTHING—and I mean NOTHING—is going to get done without a **clear goal in place and a plan for executing and achieving that goal**. I can't make it any simpler than that. Success is not just going to happen. It's up to you to make your dreams come true. And they will come true, as long as you have a plan. Make it happen!

7. SEEK ADVICE AND FEEDBACK.

There are all sorts of people out there who have your back. They are ready to support you in whatever way possible, including giving you invaluable advice and feedback. Seek it out! Listen to it! Sure, it may not be the easiest thing in the world to hear, but will it help you? Absolutely! Ask an expert. Ask a friend. Ask a relative. **I'm not kidding. People want to help. Let them!**

8. LEARN FROM YOUR MISTAKES.

Every single one of us makes mistakes. That's okay. What's not okay is if you don't learn from your mistakes and try to do better in the future. **Mistakes are the perfect opportunity to grow.** Go ahead. Make a mistake … but then be sure you learn from it, and make sure you try again. You **will** come out better for it on the other side.

9. CELEBRATE YOUR SUCCESSES AND THOSE WHO HELP YOU ALONG THE WAY.

Don't wait until everything is said and done to celebrate. Keep yourself motivated and on the right track by celebrating the small victories. Look back frequently throughout your journey and **be proud of your progress**. Did you ace the big exam you've been studying for? Great! Treat yourself to extra time with friends or download new music. And don't just celebrate yourself. Celebrate everyone who helps you along the way. Words of gratitude, a special note, or a small gesture can go a long way.

10. PAY IT FORWARD.

Remember how great it felt when someone helped you out. Remember how helpful their advice was or how encouraging their words were? Remember that? Guess what? It's your turn! You get to be someone else's mentor or role model, or just a supportive voice and friendly face along the way. Not only does it feel great when someone helps you out, but it also **feels pretty great to be the one doing the helping**.

BONUS TAKEAWAY: DARE YOURSELF!

This just might be the most important one of all. A dare may feel uncomfortable. A dare may push you out of your comfort zone. A dare may even be a little scary. Guess what? A dare may also make you stronger. A dare may also make you smarter.

A dare may also push you to be the very best you that you can possibly be. Do it!

Dare Yourself to BE WHATEVER YOU WANT, GIRL!

Last but not least ...

My dear friend,

Do you remember how I started this book by telling you something you may not have believed?

YOU ARE AMAZING!

AND YOU CAN BE WHATEVER YOU WANT, GIRL!

I hope you believe that now.

I'm going to tell you one more thing. **I'll always be here for you.** I promise. All you have to do is crack open this book.

Lots of love,

Liri

BTW, you can meet me and others like you in my Facebook group: YOU CAN BE WHATEVER YOU WANT, GIRL.

And you can find more tips and helpful advice here:

f www.facebook.com/BeWhateverYouWant.Girl
○ www.instagram.com/be_whatever_you_want_girl

BE_WHATEVER_YOU_WANT_GIRL

FlyingKids®
SPECIAL GUIDES FOR SPECIAL JOURNEYS

FlyingKids® designs and publishes unique guides for the special journeys in young readers' lives.

Whether exploring countries and cities around the world, or going on a personal journey of self-discovery, young explorers will find FlyingKids' interactive guides always take them on an exciting journey full of fun and special moments.

BE A KID OF THE WORLD

BE WHATEVER YOU WANT, GIRL!

More to come ...

For more free downloads and more activities, go to
www.theflyingkids.com

Made in the USA
Columbia, SC
12 December 2021